THIS BOOK BELONGS TO

MOTHER GOOSE

The Dainty Heron

MOTHER GOOSE

TIGER BOOKS INTERNATIONAL

LONDON

This edition published in 1994 by
Tiger Books International PLC, Twickenham, England.

© This edition Geddes & Grosset Ltd.

ISBN 1 85501 547 1

Printed in Slovenia.

CONTENTS

LIST OF ILLUSTRATIONS

THE DAYS OF CHRISTMAS

The FIRST day of Christmas,
My true love sent to me
A partridge in a pear-tree.

The SECOND day of Christmas,
My true love sent to me
Two turtle-doves and
A partridge in a pear-tree.

The THIRD day of Christmas,
My true love sent to me
Three French hens,
Two turtle-doves, and
A partridge in a pear-tree.

The FOURTH day of Christmas,
My true love sent to me
Four colly birds,
Three French hens,
Two turtle-doves, and
A partridge in a pear-tree.

The FIFTH day of Christmas,
My true love sent to me
Five gold rings,
Four colly birds,
Three French hens,
Two turtle-doves, and
A partridge in a pear-tree.

The SIXTH day of Christmas,
My true love sent to me
Six geese a-laying,
Five gold rings,
Four colly birds,
Three French hens,
Two turtle-doves, and
A partridge in a pear-tree.

The SEVENTH day of Christmas,
My true love sent to me
Seven swans a-swimming,
Six geese a-laying,
Five gold rings,
Four colly birds,
Three French hens,
Two turtle-doves, and
A partridge in a pear-tree.

The EIGHTH day of Christmas,
My true love sent to me
Eight maids a-milking,
Seven swans a-swimming,
Six geese a-laying,
Five gold rings,
Four colly birds,
Three French hens,
Two turtle-doves, and
A partridge in a pear-tree.

The NINTH day of Christmas,
My true love sent to me
Nine drummers drumming,
Eight maids a-milking,
Seven swans a-swimming,
Six geese a-laying,
Five gold rings,
Four colly birds,
Three French hens,
Two turtle-doves, and
A partridge in a pear-tree.

The TENTH day of Christmas,
My true love sent to me
Ten pipers piping,
Nine drummers drumming,
Eight maids a-milking,
Seven swans a-swimming,
Six geese a-laying,
Five gold rings,
Four colly birds,
Three French hens,
Two turtle-doves, and
A partridge in a pear-tree.

The ELEVENTH day of Christmas,
My true love sent to me
Eleven ladies dancing,
Ten pipers piping,
Nine drummers drumming,
Eight maids a-milking,
Seven swans a-swimming,
Six geese a-laying,
Five gold rings,
Four colly birds,
Three French hens,
Two turtle-doves, and
A partridge in a pear-tree.

The TWELFTH day of Christmas,
My true love sent to me
Twelve lords a-leaping,
Eleven ladies dancing,
Ten pipers piping,
Nine drummers drumming,
Eight maids a-milking,
Seven swans a-swimming,
Six geese a-laying,
Five gold rings,
Four colly birds,
Three French hens,
Two turtle-doves, and
A partridge in a pear-tree.

THE WAYS OF THE WIND

When the wind is in the East,
'T is neither good for man nor beast;
When the wind is in the North,
The skilful fisher goes not forth;
When the wind is in the South,
It blows the bait in the fishes' mouth;
When the wind is in the West
Then 't is at the very best.

THE KILKENNY CATS

There were once two cats of Kilkenny,
Each thought there was one cat too many,
So they fought and they fit,
And they scratched and they bit,
Till, excepting their nails,
And the tips of their tails,
Instead of two cats, there weren't any.

TWEEDLE-DUM AND TWEEDLE-DEE

Tweedle-dum and Tweedle-dee
Resolved to have a battle,
For Tweedle-dum said Tweedle-dee
Had spoiled his nice new rattle.

Just then flew by a monstrous crow,
As big as a tar barrel,
Which frightened both the heroes so,
They quite forgot their quarrel.

BAA, BAA, BLACK SHEEP

Baa, baa, black sheep,
Have you any wool?
Yes, marry, have I,
Three bags full:
One for my master,
One for my dame,
But none for the little boy
Who cries in the lane.

Simple Simon goes a-fishing

SIMPLE SIMON

Simple Simon met a pieman
 Going to the fair;
Says Simple Simon to the pieman,
 "Let me taste your ware."

Says the pieman unto Simon,
 "First give me a penny."
Says Simple Simon to the pieman,
 "I have not got any."

He went to try if cherries ripe
 Grew upon a thistle;
He pricked his finger very much,
 Which made poor Simon whistle.

He went for to eat honey
 Out of the mustard-pot,
He bit his tongue until he cried,
 That was all the good he got.

Simple Simon went a-fishing
 For to catch a whale;
And all the water he had got
 Was in his mother's pail.

He went to catch a dicky-bird,
    And thought he could not fail,
Because he got a little salt
    To put upon its tail.

He went to ride a spotted cow,
    That had got a little calf,
She threw him down upon the ground,
    Which made the people laugh.

Then Simple Simon went a-hunting,
    For to catch a hare,
He rode a goat about the street,
    But could not find one there.

Once Simon made a great snowball,
    And brought it in to roast;
He laid it down before the fire,
    And soon the ball was lost.

He went to take a bird's nest
    Was built upon a bough;
A branch gave way, and Simon fell
    Into a dirty slough.

He went to shoot a wild duck,
    But the wild duck flew away;
Says Simon: "I can't hit him,
    Because he will not stay."

He went to slid upon the ice,
    Before the ice would bear;
Then he plunged in above his knees,
    Which made poor Simon stare.

He went for water in a sieve,
    But soon it all ran through;
And now poor Simple Simon
    Bids you all adieu.

LITTLE MISS MUFFET

Little Miss Muffet
Sat on a tuffet,
Eating her curds and whey;
There came a big spider,
And sat down beside her,
And frightened Miss Muffet away.

TO BABYLON

How many miles is it to Babylon?
Threescore miles and ten.
Can I get there by candle-light?
Yes, and back again!
If your heels are nimble and light,
You may get there by candle-light.

BANDY LEGS

As I was going to sell my eggs
I met a man with bandy legs;
Bandy legs and crooked toes,
I tripped up his heels, and he fell on his nose.

THE CHESTNUT COLT

(The knee on which the child is sitting is to be jumped and trotted merrily)

My chestnut colt with the fairies grew,
They shod each hoof with a silver shoe;
He jumps and trots as my fair maid rides,
For twenty long miles—and more besides!

IF ALL THE SEAS WERE ONE SEA

If all the seas were one sea,
What a *great* sea that would be!
And if all the trees were on tree,
What a *great* tree that would be!
And if all the axes were one axe,
What a *great* axe that would be!
And if all the men were one man,
What a *great* man he would be!
And if the *great* man took the *great* axe
And cut down the *great* tree,
And let it fall into the *great* sea,
What a splish splash *that* would be!

DING, DONG, BELL

Ding, dong, bell,
Pussy's in the well!
Who put her in?
Little Tommy Thin.
Who pulled her out?
Little Tommy Stout.
What a naughty boy was that,
To drown poor pussy cat,
Who never did him any harm,
But killed the mice in his father's barn!

WHERE ARE YOU GOING TO, MY PRETTY MAID?

"Where are you going to, my pretty maid?"
"I'm going a-milking, sir," she said.

"May I go with you, my pretty maid?"
"You're kindly welcome, sir." she said.

"What is your father, my pretty maid?"
"My father's a farmer, sir,' she said.

"What is your fortune, my pretty maid?"
"My face is my fortune, sir," she said.

"Then I can't marry you, my pretty maid,"
"Nobody asked you, sir," she said.

THE BOY AND THE SPARROW

A little cock-sparrow sat on a green tree
and he chirruped, he chirruped, so merry was he;
A naughty boy came with his wee bow and arrow,
Determined to shoot this little cock-sparrow.
"This little cock-sparrow shall make me a stew,
and his giblets shall make me a little pie, too."
"Oh no," says the sparrow, "I won't make a stew."
So he flapped his wings and away he flew.

AN ICICLE

Lives in water,
Dies in summer,
And grows with its roots upward!

OH DEAR!

Dear, dear! what can be matter be?
Two old women got up an apple-tree;
One came down,
And the other stayed till Saturday.

LION AND UNICORN

The Lion and the Unicorn were fighting for the crown,
The Lion beat the Unicorn all round about the town.
Some gave them white bread, and some gave them brown,
Some gave them plum-cake, and sent them out of town.

CROSS-PATCH

Cross-patch, draw the latch,
Sit by the fire and spin;
Take a cup, and drink it up,
Then call the neighbours in.

A dillar, a dollar, a twelve o'clock scholar,
What makes you come so soon?
You used to come at ten o'clock
And now you come at noon!

DANCE TO YOUR DADDIE

Dance to you daddie,
My bonnie laddie;
Dance to you daddie, my bonnie lamb.
You shall get a fishy,
On a little dishy;
You shall get a fishy, when the boat comes hame.

MYSELF

As I walked by myself,
And talked to myself,
  Myself said unto me,
"Look to thyself,
Take care of thyself,
  For nobody cares for thee".

I answered myself,
And said to myself
  In the self-same repartee,
"Look to thyself,
Or not look to thyself,
  The self-same thing will be".

THREE JOLLY WELSHMEN

There were three jolly Welshmen,
    As I have heard say,
And they went a-hunting
    Upon St. David's day.

All the day they hunted,
    And nothing could they find
But a ship a-sailing,
    A-sailing with the wind.

One said it was a ship,
    The other he said "Nay";
The third he said it was a house,
    With the chimney blown away.

TOM, THE PIPER'S SON

Tom, Tom, the piper's son,
Stole a pig and away he run.
The pig was eat and Tom was beat,
And Tom went howling down the street.

One said it was a ship

ROUND THE BRAMBLE-BUSH

This is the way we wash our clothes,
  Wash our clothes, wash our clothes;
This is the way we wash our clothes
  On a cold and frosty morning!

This is the way we clean our rooms,
  Clean our rooms, clean our rooms;
This is the way we clean our rooms
  On a cold and frosty morning!

Here we go round the bramble-bush,
  The bramble-bush, the bramble-bush;
Here we go round the bramble-bush
  On a cold and frosty morning!

SNEEZING

If you sneeze on Monday, you sneeze for danger;
Sneeze on Tuesday, kiss a stranger;
Sneeze on Wednesday, sneeze for a letter;
Sneeze on Thursday, something better;
Sneeze on Friday, sneeze for sorrow;
Sneeze on Saturday, see your sweetheart tomorrow.

HANDY PANDY

Handy Pandy,
   Jack-a-Dandy,
Loves plum-cake
   and sugar-candy;
He bought some
   at a grocer's shop,
And out he came, hop, hop, hop.

ORANGES AND LEMONS

Gay go up and gay go down,
To ring the bells of London town.
Two sticks and an apple,
Say the bells at Whitechapel.
Old father Baldpate,
Say the bells at Aldgate.
Maids in white aprons,
Say the bells at St. Catherine's.
Kettles and pans,
Say the bells at St. Ann's.
Pokers and tongs,
Say the bells at St. John's.
Bulls' eyes and targets,
Say the bells at St. Marg'ret's.
Brickbat and tiles,
Say the bells of St. Giles.
Halfpence and farthings,
Say the bells of St. Martin's.
Pancakes and fritters,
Say the bells of St. Peter's.
Oranges and lemons,

Say the bells of St. Clement's.
You owe me ten shillings,
Say the bells at St. Helen's.
When will you pay me?
Say the bells of Old Bailey.
When I am rich,
Say the bells at Shoreditch.
When will that be?
Say the bells at Stepney.
I'm sure I don't know,
Says the great bell at Bow.
Here comes a candle to light you to bed,
And here comes a chopper to chop off
the last—
      last—
          last—
              man's
                  head!

THE TONGS

Long legs, crooked thighs,
Little head and no eyes.

TWO LITTLE DOGS

Two little dogs sat by the fire,
  Over a fender of coal-dust;
When one said to the other dog,
  "If Pompey won't talk, why I must."

OF ARITHMETIC

Multiplication is vexation,
  Division is as bad;
The Rule of Three doth puzzle me,
  And Practice drives me mad.

OVER THE WATER TO CHARLEY

Over the water, and over the lea,
And over the water to Charley.
Charley loves good ale and wine,
And Charley loves good brandy;
And Charley loves a pretty girl,
As sweet as sugar-candy.

Over the water, and over the sea,
And over the water to Charley,
I'll have none of your nasty beef,
Nor I'll have none of your barley;
But I'll have some of your best flour,
To make a white cake for my Charley.

THE FOX AND THE GOOSE

The fox and his wife they had a great strife,
They never ate mustard in all their whole life;
They ate their meat without fork or knife,
    And loved to be picking a bone, e-ho!

The fox jumped up on a moonlight night;
The stars they were shining, and all things bright;
"Oh, ho!" said the fox, "it's a very fine night
    For me to go through the town, e-ho!

The fox when he came to yonder stile,
He lifted his lugs and he listened a while;
"Oh, ho!" said the fox, "it's but a short mile
    From this into yonder wee town, e-ho!"

The fox when he came to the farmer's gate,
Whom should he see but the farmer's drake;
"I love you well for your master's sake,
   And long to be picking your bones, e-ho!"

The gray goose she ran round the hay-stack;
"Oh, ho!" said the fox, "you are very fat,
You'll grease my beard and ride on my back
   From this into yonder we town, e-ho!"

The farmer's wife she jumped out of bed,
And out of the window she popped her head;
"Oh, husband! oh, husband! the geese are all dead,
   For the fox has been through the town, e-ho!"

Then the old man got up in his red cap,
And swore he would catch the fox in a trap;
But the fox was too cunning, and gave him the slip,
   And ran through the town, the town, e-ho!"

When he got to the top of the hill,
He blew his trumpet both loud and shrill,
For joy that he was in safety still,
   And had got away through the town, e-ho!

When the fox came back to his den,
He had young ones both nine and ten;
"You're welcome home, daddy; you may go again,
If you bring us such fine meat from the town, e-ho!"

DICKORY, DICKORY, DOCK!

Dickory,
> Dickory,
>> Dock!
The mouse ran up the
> clock,
The clock struck
> one,
The mouse ran
> down,
Dickory,
> Dickory,
>> Dock!

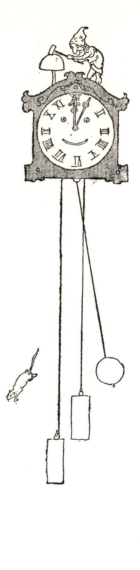

IF WISHES WERE HORSES

If wishes were horses, beggars would ride.
If turnips were watches, I'd wear one by my side.
And if "ifs" and "ands"
Were pots and pans,
There'd be no work for tinkers!

LITTLE GWEN'S JOURNEY

(The knee the child is on is to gallop briskly; then to falter, and stop.)

My little dear Gwen, she hears what I say,
We both will gallop to London in May.
Ah! cold is the water, and rough is the way,
'T is better, my baby, at home here to stay!

A AND B AND SEE

Great *A*, little *a*, bouncing B,
The cat's in the cupboard and she can't see.

THE LITTLE KITTENS

Three little kittens lost their mittens,
And they began to cry,
"Oh! Mother dear, we very much fear
That we have lost our mittens."

"Lost your mittens, you naughty kittens!
Then you shall have no pie."
  "Mee-ow, mee-ow, mee-ow."
  "No, you shall have no pie."
  "Mee-ow, mee-ow, mee-ow."

The three little kittens found their mittens,
And they began to cry,
"Oh! Mother dear, see here, see here!
See! we have found our mittens."

"Put on your mittens, you silly kittens,
And you shall have some pie.
      Purr-r, purr-r, purr-r."
      "Oh! let us have the pie.
      Purr-r, purr-r, purr-r."

The three little kittens put on their mittens,
And soon ate up the pie.
"Oh! Mother dear, we greatly fear
That we have soiled our mittens."

"Soiled your mittens, you naughty kittens!"
Then they began to sigh,
      "Mi-ow, mi-ow, mi-ow."
      Then they began to sigh,
      "Mi-ow, mi-ow, mi-ow."

The three little kittens washed their mittens,
And hung them up to dry;
"Oh! Mother dear, do you not hear
That we have washed our mittens?"

"Washed your mittens! Oh! you're good kittens.
But I smell a rat close by.
      Hush! Hush! mee-ow, mee-ow."
      "We smell a rat close by,
      Mee-ow, mee-ow, mee-ow."

BLOW, WIND, BLOW

Blow, wind, blow, and go, mill, go,
That the miller may grind his corn;
That the baker may take it,
And into rolls make it,
And send us some hot in the morn.

THE TARTS

The Queen of Hearts,
She made some tarts,
All on a summer's day;
The Knave of Hearts,
He stole those tarts,
And took them clean away.

The King of Hearts
Called for those tarts,
And beat the knave full sore.
The Knave of Hearts
Brought back those tarts,
And vowed he'd steal no more.

Blow, wind, blow!

GIRLS AND BOYS

Girls and boys, come out to play,
The moon doth shine as bright as day.

Leave your supper, and leave your sleep,
And come with your playfellows into the street.

Come with a whoop, come with a call,
come with a good will, or come not at all.

Up the ladder and down the wall,
A halfpenny roll will serve us all.

You find milk, and I'll find flour,
And we'll have a pudding in half an hour.

TWO LITTLE BIRDS

There were two blackbirds
Sat upon a hill,
The one named Jack,
The other named Jill.
Fly away, Jack!
Fly away, Jill!
Come again, Jack!
Come again, Jill.

PUSSY-CAT, PUSSY-CAT

Pussy-cat, Pussy-cat, where have you been?
I've been to London to look at the Queen.
Pussy-cat, Pussy-cat, what did you there?
I frightened a little mouse under the chair.

NEEDLES AND PINS

Needles and pins, needles and pins;
When a man marries his trouble begins.

NOTHING-AT-ALL

There was an old woman,
   called Nothing-at-all,
Who rejoiced in a dwelling
   exceedingly small;
A man stretched his mouth
   to its utmost extent,
And down at one gulp,
   house and old woman
   went.

THE MAN AND THE ROBBERS

There was a man and he had nought,
   And robbers came to rob him;
He crept up to the chimney-pot,
   And then they thought they had him.

But he got down on t'other side,
   And Then they could not find him;
He ran fourteen miles in fifteen days,
   And never looked behind him.

I LOVE SIXPENCE

I love sixpence, a jolly, jolly sixpence,
    I love sixpence as my life;
I spent a penny of it, I spent a penny of it,
    I took a penny home to my wife.

I love fourpence, a jolly, jolly fourpence,
    I love fourpence as my life;
I spent twopence of it, I spent twopence of it,
    And I took twopence home to wife.

I love nothing, a jolly, jolly nothing,
    I love nothing as my life;
I spent nothing of it, I spent nothing of it,
    I took nothing home to my wife.

ROCK-A-BY

Rock-a-by, baby, they cradle is green;
Father's a nobleman, mother's a queen;
And Betty's a lady, and wears a gold ring,
And Johnny's a drummer, and drums for the King.

Old King Cole
    Was a merry old soul,
And a merry old soul was he;
    He called for his pipe,
    And he called for his bowl,
And he called for his fiddlers three!

    Every fiddler, he had a fine fiddle,
    And a very fine fiddle had he.
Twee tweedledee, tweedledee, went the fiddlers;
    Oh, there's none so rare
    As can compare
With King Cole and his fiddlers three.

THE OLD WOMAN TOSSED IN A BLANKET

There was an old woman tossed in a basket,
    Seventeen times as high as the moon;
But where she was going no mortal could tell,
    For under her arm she carried a broom.

"Old Woman, old woman, old woman," said I,
    "Whither, oh whither, oh whither so high?"
"To sweep the cobwebs from the sky;
    And I'll be with you by and by."

THE NORTH WIND DOTH BLOW

The north wind doth blow,
And we shall have snow,
And what will poor Robin do then?
      Poor thing!

He'll sit in a barn,
And to keep himself warm,
Will hide his head under his wing,
      Poor thing!

THE DEATH AND BURIAL OF COCK ROBIN

Who killed Cock Robin?
   "I," said the Sparrow,
   "With my bow and arrow,
I killed Cock Robin."

Who saw him die?
   "I," said the Fly,
   "With my little eye,
I saw him die."

Who caught his blood?
   "I," said the Fish,
   "With my little dish,
I caught his blood."

Who'll be chief mourner?
   "I," said the Dove,
   "I mourn for my love;
I'll be chief mourner."

Who'll make his shroud?
   "I," said the Beetle,
   "With my thread and needle,
I'll make his shroud."

Who'll dig his grave?
  "I," said the Owl,
    "With my spade and trowel,
I'll dig his grave."

Who'll be the parson?
  "I," said the Rook,
    "With my little book;
I'll be the parson."

Who'll be the clerk?
  "I," said the Lark,
    "I'll say Amen in the dark;
I'll be the clerk."

Who'll bear the torch?
  "I," said the Linnet,
    "I'll come in a minute;
I'll bear the torch."

Who'll sing his dirge?
  "I," said the Thrush,
    "As I sing in the bush,
I'll sing his dirge."

Who'll bear the pall?
   "We," said the Wren,
    Both the Cock and Hen,
"We'll bear the pall."

Who'll carry his coffin?
   "I," said the Kite,
   "If it be in the night,
I'll carry his coffin."

Who'll toll the bell?
   "I," said the Bull,
    "Because I can pull,
I'll toll the bell."

All the birds of the air
   Fell a-sighing and a-sobbing
   When they heard the bell toll
For poor Cock Robin.

SING A SONG OF SIXPENCE

Sing a song of sixpence,
    Pockets full of rye;
Four-and-twenty blackbirds
    Baked in a pie.

When the pie was opened
    The birds began to sing:
Was not that a dainty dish
    To set before the king?

The king was in his counting-house
    Counting out his money;
The queen was in the parlour
    Eating bread and honey.

The maid was in the garden
    Hanging out the clothes;
Down came a blackbird
    And snapped of her nose.

GOING TO ST. IVES

As I was going to St. Ives
I met a man with seven wives.
Every wife had seven sacks,
Every sack had seven cats,
Every cat had seven kits,
Kits, cats, sacks, and wives,
How many were going to St. Ives?

TO BED!

"Come let's to bed,"
Says Sleepy-head;
"Sit up a while," says Slow;
"Put on the pan,"
Says Greedy Nan,
"Let's sup before we go."

MY MAID MARY

My maid Mary she minds the dairy,
While I go a-hoeing and mowing each morn;
Gaily run the reel and the little spinning-wheel,
Whilst I am singing and mowing my corn.

FOUR & TWENTY TAILORS

Four & twenty tailors went to kill a snail;
    The bravest man amongst them
Durst not touch her tail.

She put out her horns,
    Like a little Kerry Cow.

Run, Tailors, Run!
She'll catch you
    just now!

ONE MISTY MOISTY MORNING

One misty moisty morning,
When cloudy was the weather,
There I met an old man
Clothed all in leather;
Clothed all in leather,
With a strap below his chin—
How do you do? and how do you do?
And how do you do again?

London Bridge

London Bridge is broken down,
    Dance o'er my Lady Lee;
London Bridge is broken down,
    With a gay lady.

How shall we build it up again?
    Dance o'er my Lady Lee;
How shall be build it up again?
    With a gay lady.

Silver and gold will be stolen away,
    Dance o'er my Lady Lee;
Silver and gold will be stolen away,
    With a gay lady.

Build it up with iron bars,
    Dance o'er my Lady Lee;
Build it up with iron bars,
    With a gay lady.

Iron bars will rust and break,
    Dance o'er my Lady Lee;
Iron bars will rust and break,
    With a gay lady.

Build it up with wood and clay,
    Dance o'er my Lady Lee;
Build it up with wood and clay,
    With a gay lady.

Wood and clay will wash away,
    Dance o'er my Lady Lee;
Wood and clay will wash away,
    With a gay lady.

Build it up with stone so strong,
    Dance o'er my Lady Lee;
Huzza! 't will last for ages long,
    With a gay lady.

If all the World were Apple Pie
And all the Sea were Ink,
And all the trees were Bread and Cheese,
What should we have to Drink?

LITTLE BO-PEEP

Little Bo-Peep has lost her sheep,
    And can't tell where to find them;
Leave them alone, and they'll come home,
    And bring their tails behind them.

Little Bo-Peep fell fast asleep,
    And dreamt she heard them bleating;
But when she awoke, she found it a joke,
    For still they were all fleeting.

Then up she took her little crook,
  Determined for to find them;
She found them indeed, but it made her heart bleed,
  For they'd left all their tails behind them.

It happened one day, as Bo-Peep did stray
  Into a meadow hard by,
There she espied their tails side by side,
  All hung on a tree to dry.

She heaved a sigh, and wiped her eye,
  And went over hill and dale, oh'
And tried what she could, as a shepherdess should,
  To tack to each sheep its tail, oh!

GRANNY'S LULLABY

(The child is to be hushed in the arms.)

Sing gentle songs to thy granny, darling,
Thy granny shall sing to thee;
To no one else doth it matter, darling,
  So, baby dear, stay with me!

HUSH-A-BYE

Hush-a-bye, baby,
  On the tree-top!
When the wind blows
  The cradle will rock.

When the bough breaks
  The cradle will fall.
Down tumbles baby,
  And cradle and all.

BOYS AND GIRLS

What are little boys made of, made of,
What are little boys made of?
Snips and snails, and puppy-dogs' tails;
That's what little boys are made of, made of.

What are little girls made of, made of,
What are little girls made of?
Sugar and spice, and all things nice;
That's what little girls are made of, made of.

Hush-a-bye, baby

LITTLE POLLY FLINDERS

Little Polly Flinders
Sat among the cinders,
Warming her pretty little toes;
Her mother came and caught her,
And whipped her little daughter
For spoiling her nice new clothes.

Little Polly Flinders

The Piper's Son

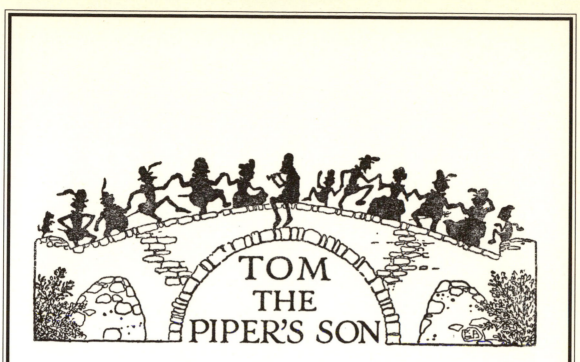

Tom, Tom the piper's son,
He learned to play when he was young;
But all the tune that he could play
Was "Over the hills and far away".
Over the hills and a great way off,
And the wind will blow my top-knot off.

Now Tom with his pipe made such a noise
That he pleased both the girls and boys;
And they stopped to hear him play
"Over the hills and far away".

Tom with his pipe did play with such skill
That those who heard him could never stand still;
Whenever they heard they began for to dance—
Even pigs on their hind legs would after him prance.

As Dolly was milking the cow one day,
Tom took out his pipe and began for to play;
So Doll and the cow danced "The Cheshire Round"
Till the pail was broke and the milk ran on the ground.

He met old Dame Trot with a basket of eggs;
He used his pipe and she used her legs.
She danced about till the eggs were broke;
She began for to fret, but he laughed at the joke.

He saw a cross fellow was beating an ass
That was laden with pots, pans, dishes, and glass;
He took out his pipe and played them a tune,
And the jackass's load was lightened full soon.

CURLY-LOCKS

Curly-locks, Curly-locks, wilt thou be mine?
Thou shalt not wash the dishes, nor yet feed the swine;
But sit on a cushion, and sew a fine seam,
And feed upon strawberries, sugar, and cream.

GEORGY PORGY

Georgy Porgy, pudding and pie,
Kiss'd the girls and made them cry.
When the boys came out to play,
Georgy Porgy ran away.

THE LITTLE NUT TREE

I had a little nut tree; nothing would it bear
But a silver nutmeg and a golden pear.
The King of Spain's daughter came to see me,
And all was because of my little nut tree.
I skipped over water, I danced over sea,
And all the birds in the air couldn't catch me.

Lucy Locket lost her pocket,
Kitty Fisher found it.
There was not a penny in it,
Just the ribbon round it!

GOOSEY, GOOSEY, GANDER

Goosey, goosey, gander,
　Whither dost thou wander?
Upstairs and downstairs,
　And in my lady's chamber.

There I met an old man
　That would not say his prayers;
I took him by the left leg,
　And threw him downstairs.

TEN FINGERS

One, two, three, four, five
Once I caught a fish alive,

Six, seven, eight, nine, ten,
But I let him go again.

Why did you let him go?
Because he bit my finger so.

Which finger did he bite?
The little one upon the right.

ONE, TWO

One, two, buckle my shoe;
Three, four, knock at the door;
Five, six, pick up sticks;
Seven, eight, lay them straight;
Nine, ten, a good fat hen;
Eleven, twelve, who will delve;
Thirteen, fourteen, maids a-courting;
Fifteen, sixteen, maids in the kitchen;
Seventeen, eighteen, maids a-waiting;
Nineteen, twenty, my plate's empty.

THREE CROWS

There were three crows sat on a stone,
　　　Fal, la, la la lal de,
Two flew away, and then there was one,
　　　Fal, la, la la lal de,
The other crow finding himself alone,
　　　Fal, la, la la lal de,
He flew away, and then there was none,
　　　Fal, la, la la lal de.

TO MARKET! TO MARKET!

To market! to market
To buy a fat pig.
Home again! home again!
Jiggety-jig.

To market! to market
To buy a fat hog.
Home again! home again!
Jiggety-jog.

A Farmer went Trotting

A farmer went trotting upon his grey mare,
 Bumpety, bumpety, bump!
With his daughter behind him so rosy and fair,
 Lumpety, lumpety, lump!
A raven cried "croak" and they all tumbled down,
 Bumpety, bumpety, bump!

The mare broke her knees, and the farmer his crown,
 Lumpety, lumpety, lump!
The mischievous raven flew laughing away,
 Bumpety, bumpety, bump!
And vowed he would serve them the same the next day,
 Lumpety, lumpety, lump!

Little Boy Blue

Little Boy Blue, come, blow up your horn!
The sheep's in the meadow, the cow's in the corn.
Where's the little boy that looks after the sheep?
Under the haystack fast asleep.

THE MAN IN THE MOON

The Man in the Moon came tumbling down,
And asked the way to Norwich;
He went by the south, and burnt his mouth
With eating cold pease porridge.

BABY BUNTING

Baby, baby bunting
Father's gone a-hunting,
Mother's gone a-milking,
Sister's gone a-silking,
Brother's gone to buy a skin
To wrap the baby bunting in.

TWO T's

Thomas a' Tattamus took two T's
To tie two tups to two tall trees,
To frighten the terrible Thomas a' Tattamus.
Tell me how many T's there are in all that.

He went by the south

MARY'S LAMB

Mary had a little lamb,
　　Its fleece was white as snow;
And everywhere that Mary went
　　The lamb was sure to go.

He followed her to school one day;
　　That was against the rule;
It made the children laugh and play
　　To see a lamb at school.

And so the teacher turned him out,
　　But still he lingered near,
And waited patiently about
　　Till Mary did appear.

Then he ran to her, and laid
　　His head upon her arm,
As if he said, "I'm not afraid,
　　You'll keep me from all harm."

"What makes the lamb love Mary so?"
　　The eager children cry.
"Oh, Mary loves the lamb, you know,"
　　The teacher did reply.

And you each gentle animal
In confidence may bind,
And make it follow at your will,
If you are only kind.

THE WIDOW OF BABYLON

Here comes a poor widow from Babylon,
With six poor children all alone,
One can bake, and one can brew,
One can shape, and one can sew;
One of them can dance and sing,
One can bake a cake for the king.
Come choose you east, come choose you west,
Come choose the one that you love best.

WEE WILLIE WINKIE

Wee Willie Winkie runs through the town,
Upstairs and downstairs in his night-gown;
Rapping at the window, crying through the lock,
"Are the children in their beds, for it's past eight o'clock?"

COCK-A-DOODLE-DOO!

Cock-a-doodle-doo!
My dame has lost her shoe;
My master's lost his fiddle-stick,
And don't know what to do.

Cock-a-doodle-doo!
What is my dame to do?
Till master finds his fiddle-stick,
She'll dance without her shoe.

TWINKLE, TWINKLE, LITTLE STAR

Twinkle, twinkle, little star,
How I wonder what you are!
Up above the world so high,
Like a diamond in the sky.

When the blazing sun is gone,
When he nothing shines upon,
Then you show your little light,
Twinkle, twinkle, all the night.

Then the traveller in the dark
Thanks you for your tiny spark;
How could he see where to go,
If you did not twinkle so?

In the dark blue sky you keep,
Often through my curtains peep,
For you never shut your eye,
Till the sun is in the sky.

How your bright and tiny spark
Lights the traveller in the dark!
Though I know not what you are,
Twinkle, twinkle, little star.

THE OLD WOMAN WHO LIVED IN A SHOE

There was an old woman who lived in a shoe,
She had so many children she didn't know what to do;
She gave them some broth, without any bread,
She whipped them all round, and sent them to bed.

SOLOMON GRUNDY

Solomon Grundy,
Born on a Monday,
Christened on Tuesday,
Married on Wednesday,
Took ill on Thursday,
Worse on Friday,
Died on Saturday,
Buried on Sunday,
This is the end
Of Solomon Grundy.

The Old Woman who lived in a Shoe

The Little Man and his Gun

DIDDLE DIDDLE DUMPLING

Diddle diddle dumpling, my son John
Went to bed with his breeches on,
One stocking off and one stocking on,
Diddle diddle dumpling, my son John.

THERE WAS A LITTLE MAN

There was a little man, and he had a little gun,
And his bullets they were made of lead, lead, lead.
He shot Johnny Spring through the middle of his wig,
And knocked it right off his head, head, head.

HARK! HARK!

Hark! hark! the dogs do bark,
   The beggars have come to town;
Some in jags, and some in rags,
   And some in velvet gown.

CHRISTMAS

Christmas comes but once a year,
And when it comes it brings good cheer.

RIDDLES

With Picture Answers

Old Mother Twitchett had but one eye,
And a long tail which she let fly;
And every time she went
    over a gap,
She left a bit of her tail
    in a trap.

Made long ago, yet made to-day,
Employed while others sleep;
What few would like to
    give away
And none would wish to
    keep.

Humpty Dumpty sat on a wall,
Humpty Dumpty had a great fall;
All the king's horses and
    all the king's men
Cannot put Humpty
    Dumpty together
    again.

I Saw a Ship a-sailing

I saw a ship a-sailing,
    A-sailing on the sea;
And it was full of pretty things
    For baby and for me.

There were sweetmeats in the cabin,
    And apples in the hold;
The sails were made of silk,
    And the masts were made of gold.

The four-and-twenty sailors
    That stood upon the decks,
Were four-and-twenty white mice,
    With chains about their necks.

The captain was a duck,
    With a packet on his back;
And when the ship began to move,
    The captain cried "Quack! quack!"

The Boy in the Barn

A little boy went into a barn,
    And lay down on some hay.
An owl came out, and flew about,
    And the little boy ran away.

I saw a ship a-sailing

THE SPIDER AND THE FLY

"Will you walk into my parlour?"
  Said the spider to the fly;
"'T is the prettiest little parlour
  That ever you did spy.
The way into my parlour
  Is up a winding stair;
And I have many curious things
  To show you when you're there."
"Oh, no, no," said the little fly;
  "To ask me is in vain;
For who goes up your winding stair
  Can ne'er come down again."

"I'm sure you must be weary, dear,
  With soaring up so high;
Will you rest upon my little bed?"
  Said the spider to the fly.
"There are pretty curtains drawn around;
  The sheets are fine and thin;
And if you like to rest awhile,
  I'll snugly tuck you in!"
"Oh, no, no," said the little fly;
  "For I've often heard it said,
They never, never wake again,
  Who sleep upon your bed!"

Said the cunning spider to the fly,
  "Dear friend, what can I do
To prove the warm affection
  I've always felt for you?"
"I thank you, gentle sir," she said,
  "For what you're pleased to say,
And bidding you good morning now,
  I'll call another day."

And now, dear little children,
  Who may this story read,
To idle, silly, flattering words,
  I pray you ne'er give heed.

Unto an evil counsellor
  Close heart and ear and eye,
And take a lesson from this tale
  Of the Spider and the Fly.

THE HART

The hart he loves the high wood,
  The hare she loves the hill;
The knight he loves his bright sword,
  The lady—loves her will.

PAT-A-CAKE, PAT-A-CAKE

Pat-a-cake, pat-a-cake, baker's man!
(So I will, master, as fast as I can.)
Pat it, and prick it, and mark it with T;
Put in the oven for Tommy and me.

My Boy Tammie

"Where have you been all day,
    My boy Tammie?"
"I've been all the day
Courting of a lady gay;
But oh! she's too young
To be taken from her mammy."

"What work can she do,
    My boy Tammie?
Can she bake and can she brew,
    My boy Tammie?"

"She can brew and she can bake,
And she can make our wedding cake:
But oh! she's too young
To be taken from her mammy."

"What age may she be?
What age may she be?
    My boy Tammie?"

"Twice two, twice seven,
Twice ten, twice eleven"
But oh, she's too young
To be taken from her mammy."

I'LL TELL YOU A STORY

I'll tell you a story
About Jack Nory—
And now my story's begun:
I'll tell you another,
About Jack his brother—
And now my story's done.

Peter White can
ne'er go right —
Would you know
the reason why?
He follows his nose
Wherever he goes,
And that
stands all
awry!

H G C
Marsh
Lambert

Man and Wife

There was an old man, who lived in a wood,
    As you may plainly see;
He said he could do as much work in a day,
    As his wife could do in three.
"With all my heart," the old woman said:
    "If that you will allow,
To-morrow you'll stay at home in my stead,
    And I'll go drive the plough."

"But you must milk the Tidy cow,
　　For fear that she go dry;
And you must feed the little pigs
　　That are within the sty;
And you must mind the speckled hen,
　　For fear she lay away;
And you must reel the spool of yarn
　　That I spun yesterday."

The old woman took a staff in her hand,
　　And went to drive the plough;
The old man took a pail in his hand,
　　And went to milk the cow;
But Tidy hinched, and Tidy flinched,
　　And Tidy broke his nose,
And Tidy gave him such a blow,
　　That the blood ran down to his toes.

"High! Tidy! ho! Tidy! High!
　Tidy, do stand still!
If ever I milk you, Tidy, again,
　'T will be sore against my will."
He went to feed the little pigs
　That were within the sty;
He hit his head against the beam,
　And he made the blood to fly.

He went to mind the speckled hen,
　For fear she'd laid astray,
And he forgot the spool of yarn
　His wife spun yesterday.
So he swore by the sun, the moon, and the stars,
　And the green leaves on the tree,
　If his wife didn't do a day's work in her life,
She should ne'er be ruled by he.

ABC

A,B,C, tumble down D,
The cat's in the cupboard and can't see me!

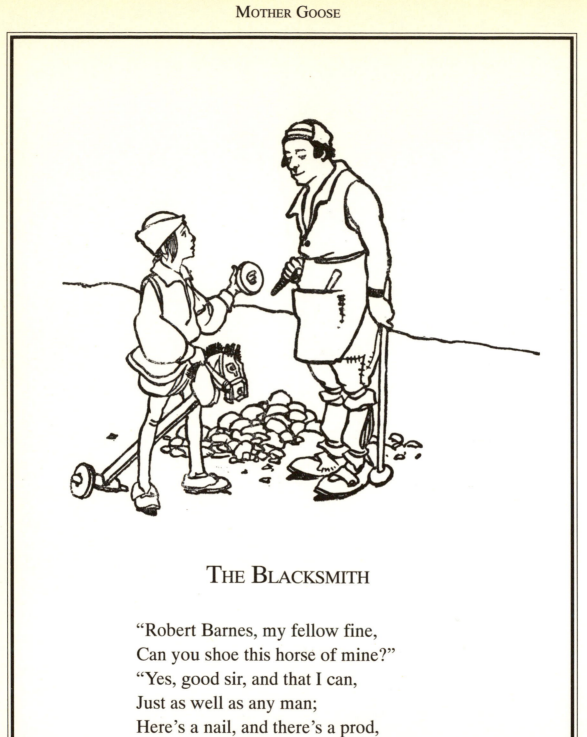

THE BLACKSMITH

"Robert Barnes, my fellow fine,
Can you shoe this horse of mine?"
"Yes, good sir, and that I can,
Just as well as any man;
Here's a nail, and there's a prod,
And now, good sir, your horse is shod."

LADY-BIRD

Lady-bird, Lady-bird, fly away home,
Your house is on fire, your children
  have gone,
All but one that lies under a stone;
Fly thee home, Lady-bird, ere it be
  gone.

MY LITTLE OLD MAN AND I

My little old man and I fell out;
I'll tell you what 't was all about:
I had money and he had none,
And that's the way the noise begun.

HEY! DIDDLE, DIDDLE

Hey! diddle, diddle,
The cat and the fiddle,
The cow jumped over the moon;
The little dog laughed
To see such sport,
While the dish ran away with the spoon.

THE OLD WOMAN OF NORWICH

There was an old woman of Norwich,
Who lived upon nothing but porridge;
Parading the town,
She turned cloak into gown,
This thrifty old woman of Norwich.

JACK AND JILL

Jack and Jill went up the hill
   To fetch a pail of water.
Jack fell down and broke his crown,
   And Jill came tumbling after.

Then up Jack got and off did trot,
   As fast as he could caper,
To old Dame Dob, who patched his nob
   With vinegar and brown paper.

LITTLE TOM TUCKER

Little Tom Tucker sings for
   his supper.

What shall he eat?
   White bread and butter.

How will he cut it without
   e'er a knife?

How will he be married
   without e'er a wife?

THE MAN OF THESSALY

There was a man of Thessaly,
   And he was wond'rous wise,
He jump'd into a quickset hedge,
   And scratched out both his eyes.

But when he saw his eyes were out,
   With all his might and main
He jump'd into another hedge,
   And scratched them back again.

THERE WAS A LITTLE GIRL

There was a little girl
Who had a little curl
Right down the middle of her forehead;
And when she was good
She was very, very good,
And when she was bad she was horrid.

THE HOUSE THAT JACK BUILT

This is the House that Jack built.

This is the Malt
That lay in the house that Jack built.

This is the Rat
That ate the malt,
That lay in the house that Jack built.

This is the Cat
That killed the rat,
That ate the malt,
That lay in the house that Jack built.

This is the Dog
That worried the cat,
That killed the rat,
That ate the malt,
That lay in the house that Jack built.

This is the Cow with the crumpled horn
That tossed the dog,
That worried the cat,
That killed the rat,
That ate the malt,
That lay in the house that Jack built.

This is the Maiden all forlorn
That milked the cow with the crumpled horn,
That tossed the dog,
That worried the cat,
That killed the rat,
That ate the malt,
That lay in the house that Jack built.

This is the Man all tattered and torn
That kissed the maiden all forlorn,
That milked the cow with the crumpled horn,
That tossed the dog,
That worried the cat,
That killed the rat,
That ate the malt,
That lay in the house that Jack built.

This is the Priest all shaven and shorn
That married the Man all tattered and torn,
That kissed the maiden all forlorn,
That milked the cow with the crumpled horn,
That tossed the dog,
That worried the cat,
That killed the rat,
That ate the malt,
That lay in the house that Jack built.

This is the Cock that crowed in the morn
That waked the priest all shaven and shorn,
That married the Man all tattered and torn,
That kissed the maiden all forlorn,
That milked the cow with the crumpled horn,
That tossed the dog,
That worried the cat,
That killed the rat,
That ate the malt,
That lay in the house that Jack built.

This is the Farmer that sowed the corn
That kept the cock that crowed in the morn,
That waked the priest all shaven and shorn,
That married the Man all tattered and torn,
That kissed the maiden all forlorn,
That milked the cow with the crumpled horn,
That tossed the dog,
That worried the cat,
That killed the rat,
That ate the malt,
That lay in the house that Jack built.

SULKY SUE

Here's Sulky Sue.
What shall we do?
Turn her face to the wall
Till she comes to.

JUMPING JOAN

Here am I, little Jumping Joan,
When nobody's with me, I'm always alone.

THE DAYS OF THE MONTH

Thirty days hath September,
April, June, and November,
All the rest have thirty-one
Excepting February alone,
With hath twenty-eight days clear,
And twenty-nine in each Leap Year.

THE LITTLE HUSBAND

I had a little husband,
    No bigger than my thumb;
I put him in a pint pot,
    And I bade him drum.

I bought a little horse,
    That galloped up and down;
I bridled him, and saddled him,
    And sent him out of town.

I gave him a pair of garters
    To tie up his little hose,
And a little silk handkerchief
    To wipe his little nose.

JACK SPRAT'S PIG

Jack Sprat had a pig,
Who was not very little, nor yet very big;
He was not very lean, he was not very fat;
"He'll do well for a grunt," says little Jack Sprat.

AS I WAS GOING ALONG

As I was going along,
      along,
A-singing a comical song,
      song, song,
The lane that I went was
      so long, long, long,
And the song that I sang
      was so long, long, long,
And so I went singing
      along.

JOHNNY

Johnny shall have a new bonnet,
      And Johnny shall go to the fair,
And Johnny shall have a new ribbon,
      To tie up his bonny brown hair.

UP PIPPEN HILL

As I was going up Pippen HIll,
    Pippen HIll was dirty;
There I met a pretty miss,
    And she dropped me a curtsey.

Little miss, pretty miss,
    Blessings light upon you!
If I had half a crown a day,
    I'd spend it all upon you.

DOCTOR FOSTER

Doctor Foster went to Glo'ster.
In a shower of rain;
He stepped in a puddle right up to his middle,
And never went there again.

TOMMY TITTLEMOUSE

Little Tommy Tittlemouse
Lived in a little house;
He caught fishes
In other men's ditches.

LUBIN LOO

Here we go Lubin Loo,
 Here we go Lubin light,
Here we go Lubin Loo
 All on a Saturday night.

Put your right hand in,
 Put your right hand out,
Shake it a little, a little,
 And turn yourself about.
 (*The same for your left hand.*)

Put your right ear in,
 Put your right ear out,
Shake it a little, a little,
 And turn yourself about.
 (*The same for your left ear.*)

Put your right foot in,
 Put your right foot out,
Shake it a little, a little,
 And turn yourself about.
 (*The same for your left foot.*)

Put yourself in,
 Put yourself out,
Shake just a little, a little,
 And turn yourself about.

Mary, Mary, Quite Contrary

Mary, Mary, quite contrary, how does
    your garden grow?
Silver bells and cockle-shells, and pretty maids
    all in a row.

SWAN

Swan, swan, over the sea;
Swim, swan, swim!
Swan, swan, back again;
Well swum, swan!

THE MAN IN THE WILDERNESS

The man in the wilderness said to me
"How many strawberries grew in the sea?"
I answere him, as I thought good,
As many as red herrings grew in the wood.

DAFFY-DOWN-DILLY

Daffy-down-dilly has come to town,
In a yellow petticoat, and a green gown.

AN EASTER SAYING

The rose is red, the violet's blue;
The gillyflower's sweet, and so are you.
There are the words you bade me say
For a pair of new gloves on Easter Day.

BANBURY CROSS

Ride a cock-horse to Banbury Cross,
To see a fine lady upon a white horse.
Rings on her fingers, bells on her toes,
She shall have music wherever she goes.

I LIKE LITTLE PUSSY

I LIKE little pussy, her coat is so
warm,
And if I don't hurt her she'll do
me no harm;
So I'll not pull her tail, nor drive
her away,
But Pussy and I very gently will
play.

ALL FOR WANT OF A NAIL

For want of a nail, the shoe was lost,
For want of the shoe, the horse was lost,
For want of the horse, the rider was lost,
For want of the rider, the battle was lost,
For want of the battle, the kingdom was lost,
And all for the want of a horse-shoe nail!

THE WISE MEN OF GOTHAM

Three wise men of Gotham,
They went to sea in a bowl;
And if the bowl had been stronger
My song had been longer.

The Wise Men of Gotham

The Frog he would a-wooing go

A FROG HE WOULD A WOOING GO

A frog he would a-wooing go,
   Heigh-ho, says Rowley!
Whether his mother would let him or no.
   With a rowley powley, gammon and spinach,
   Heigh-ho, says Anthony Rowley!

So off he set with his opera hat,
   Heigh-ho, says Rowley!
And on the road he met with a rat.
   With a rowley powley, &c.

"Pray, Mr. Rat, will you go with me,"
   Heigh-ho, says Rowley!
"Kind Mrs. Mousey for to see?"
   With a rowley powley, &c.

When they came to the door of Mousey's hall,
    Heigh-ho, says Rowley!
They gave a loud knock, and they gave a loud call.
    With a rowley powley, &c.

"Pray, Mrs. Mouse, are you within?"
    Heigh-ho, says Rowley!
"Oh yes, kind sirs, I'm sitting to spin."
    With a rowley powley, &c.

"Pray, Mrs. Mouse, will you give us some beer?"
    Heigh-ho, says Rowley!
"For Froggy and I are fond of good cheer."
    With a rowley powley, &c.

But while they were all a merry-making,
    Heigh-ho, says Rowley!
A cat and her kittens came tumbling in.
    With a rowley powley, &c.

The cat she seized the rat by the crown;
    Heigh-ho, says Rowley!
The kittens they pulled the little mouse down.
    With a rowley powley, &c.

This put Mr. Frog in a terrible fright;
    Heigh-ho, says Rowley!
He took up his hat, and he wished them good-night.
    With a rowley powley, &c.

But as Froggy was crossing over a brook,
    Heigh-ho, says Rowley!
A lily-white duck came and gobbled him up.
    With a rowley powley, &c.

HIGGLEY-PIGGLEY

Higgley-Piggley, my black hen,
She lays eggs for gentlemen;
Gentlemen come every day
To see what my black hen doth lay.

BELL HORSES

Bell horses, bell horses, what time of day,
One o'clock, two o'clock, three and away.

THREE BLIND MICE

Three blind mice, see how they run!
They all ran after the farmer's wife,
Who cut off their tails with a carving knife,
Did ever you see such a thing in your life
As three blind mice?

FINGERS AND TOES

Every lady in this land
Has twenty nails upon each hand;
Five and twenty on hands and feet.
All this is true, without deceit.

THE MAN AND HIS CALF

There was an old man,
    And he had a calf,
    And that's half;
He took him out of the stall,
And put him on the wall,
    And that's all.

POLLY AND SUKEY

Polly, put the kettle on,
Polly, put the kettle on,
Polly, put the kettle on,
        And we'll have tea.

Sukey, take it off again,
Sukey, take it off again,
Sukey, take it off again,
        They're all gone away.

THE CARRION CROW

A carrion crow sat on an oak,
    Fol de riddle, lol de riddle, hi ding do,
Watching a tailor shape his cloak;
Sing heigh ho, the carrion crow,
    Fol de riddle, lol de riddle, hi ding do.

THREE MEN IN A TUB

Rub-a-dub-dub!
Three men in a tub;
And who do you think
they be?
The butcher, the baker,
The candlestick-maker;
Turn 'em out, knaves all
three!

DANCE, LITTLE BABY

Dance, little Baby, dance up high!
Never mind, Baby, Mother is by;
Crow and caper, caper and crow,
There, little Baby, there you go!
Up to the ceiling, down to the ground,
Backwards and forwards, round and round;
Dance, little Baby, and Mother will sing,
With the merry coral, ding, ding, ding.

A WEEK OF BIRTHDAYS

Monday's child is fair of face,
Tuesday's child is full of grace,
Wednesday's child is full of woe,
Thursday's child has far to go,
Friday's child is loving and giving,
Saturday's child works hard for its living,
But the child that is born on the Sabbath day
Is bonny, and blithe, and good, and gay.

THERE WAS AN OLD WOMAN

There was an old woman, and what do you think?
She live upon nothing but victuals and drink;
And tho' victuals and drink were the chief of her diet,
This plaguy old woman could never keep quiet.
She went to the baker to buy her some bread,
And when she came home her old husband was dead;
She went to the clerk to toll the bell,
And when she came back, her old husband was well.

THE MONTHS

January brings the snow,
Makes our feet and fingers glow.

February brings the rain,
Thaws the frozen lake again.

March brings breezes loud and shrill,
To stir the dancing daffodil.

April brings the primrose sweet,
Scatters daisies at our feet.

May brings flocks of pretty lambs,
Skipping by their fleecy dams.

June brings tulips, lilies, roses,
Fills the children's hands with posies.

Hot July brings cooling showers,
Apricots and gillyflowers.

August brings the sheaves of corn,
Then the harvest home is borne.

Warm September brings the fruit,
Sportsmen then begin to shoot.

Fresh October brings the pheasant,
Then to gather nuts is pleasant.

Dull November brings the blast,
Then the leaves are whirling fast.

Chill December brings the sleet,
Blazing fire and Christmas treat.

THE WREN AND THE DOVE

The Dove says, coo! coo! what shall I do?
I can scarce maintain two.
Pooh! Pooh! says the wren, I have got ten,
And keep them all like gentlemen.

Bow-wow, says the Dog

Bow-wow, says the dog;
  Mew-mew, says the cat;
Grunt, grunt, goes the hog;
  And squeak, goes the rat.

Chirp, chirp, says the sparrow,
  Caw, caw, says the crow;
Quack, quack, says the duck;
  And what cuckoos say, you
    know.

So, with sparrows and cuckoos,
  With rats and with dogs,
With ducks and with crows,
  With cats and with hogs,

A fine song I have made,
  To please you, my dear;
And if it's well sung,
  'T will be charming to hear.

If

If you are to be gentleman, as I suppose you be,
You'll neither laugh nor smile for a tickling of the knee.

FOR EVERY EVIL

For every evil under the sun
There is a remedy or there is none.
If there be one, seek till you find it;
If there be none, well never mind it.

A SWARM OF BEES

A swarm of bees in May
Is worth a load of hay;
A swarm of bees in June
Is worth a silver spoon;
A swarm of bees in July
Is not worth a fly.

THE CUCKOO

In April,
Come he will.
In May,
He sings all day.
In June,
He changes his tune.
In July,
He makes ready to fly.
In August,
Go he must.

I HAD A LITTLE PONY

I had a little pony,
    His name was Dapple Gray;
I lent him to a lady,
    To ride a mile away.
She whipped him, she lashed him,
    She drove him through the mire;
I would not lend my pony now,
    For all the lady's hire.

THE MILLER OF DEE

There was a jolly miller once
    Lived on the river Dee:
He worked and sang from morn till night,
    No lark so blithe as he.

And this the burden of his song
    For ever used to be:
"I care for nobody! no! not I!
    And nobody cares for me!"

I lent him to a lady

THE LITTLE MAN AND HIS LITTLE GUN

There was a little man, and he had a little gun,
   And his bullets were made of lead, lead lead;
He went to the brook, and saw a little duck,
   And shot it right through the head, head, head.

He carried it home to his old wife Joan,
   And told her a fire to make, make, make,
To roast the little duck he had shot in the brook,
   And he'd go and fetch the drake, drake, drake.

The drake was a-swimming, with his curly tail;
   The little man made it his mark, mark, mark.
He let off his gun, but he fired too soon,
   And the drake flew away with a quack, quack,
   quack.

The Little Man and the Drake

LITTLE JACK HORNER

Little Jack Horner sat in a corner,
    Eating a Christmas pie;
He put in his thumb, and pulled out a plum,
    And said: "What a good boy am I!"

CAESAR'S SONG

Bow, wow, wow, whose dog art thou?
Little Tom Tinker's dog, bow, wow, wow.

THE FIFTH OF NOVEMBER

Please to remember the fifth of November,
    Gunpowder treason and plot;
I see no reason why Gunpowder treason
    Should ever be forgot.

        Guy, guy, guy,
        Stick him up on high,
        Put him on the bonfire,
        And there let him die!

THE KING OF FRANCE

The King of France went up the hill
    With twenty thousand men,
The King of France came down the hill,
    And ne'er went up again.

THE MIST

A hill full, a hole full,
Yet you cannot catch a bowl full.

ONE, TWO, THREE AND FOUR LEGS

Two legs sat upon three legs
With one leg in this lap;
In comes four legs,
And runs away with one leg;
Up jumps two legs,
Catches up three legs,
Throws it after four legs,
And makes him bring back one leg.

OLD MOTHER HUBBARD

Old Mother Hubbard
Went to her cupboard,
   To give her poor dog a bone;
But when she go there
The cupboard was bare,
   And so the poor Dog had none.

She went to the baker's
   To buy him some bread,
When she came back
   The Dog was dead.

She went to the undertaker's
   To buy him a coffin,
When she came back
   The Dog was laughing.

She went to the tailor's
  To buy him a coat,
When she came back
  He was riding a goat.

She went to the cobbler's
  To buy him some shoes,
When she came back
  He was reading the news.

She went to the sempster's
  To buy him some linen,
When she came back
  The Dog was a-spinning.

She took a clean dish
    To get him some tripe,
When she came back
    He was smoking his pipe.

She went to the alehouse
    To get him some beer,
When she came back
    The Dog sat in a chair.

She went to the tavern
    For white wine and red,
When she came back
    The Dog stood on his head.

She went to the hatter's
    To buy him a hat,
When she came back
    He was feeding the cat.

She went to the barber's
    To buy him a wig,
When she came back
    He was dancing a jig.

She went to the fruiterer's
　　To buy him some fruit,
When she came back
　　He was playing the flute.

She went to the hosier's
　　To buy him some hose,
When she came back
　　He was dressed in his clothes.

The Dame made a curtsey,
　　The Dog make a bow;
The Dame said, "Your servant",
　　The Dog said, "Bow-wow".

SAINT SWITHIN'S DAY

St. Swithin's day, if thou dost rain,
For forty days it will remain;
St. Swithin's day, if thou be fair,
For forty days 't will rain no more.

BOBBY SHAFT

Bobby Shaft is gone to sea,
With silver buckles at his knee;
When he'll come home he'll marry me,
Pretty Bobby Shaft!

Bobby Shaft is fat and fair,
Combing down his yellow hair;
He's my love for evermore!
Pretty Bobby Shaft!

MARGERY DAW

SEE-SAW, Margery Daw,
    Jacky shall have a new master.
He shall have but a penny a day,
    Because he can't work any faster.

COCK ROBIN'S COURTING

Cock Robin got up early,
    At the break of day,
And went to Jenny's window
    To sing a roundelay.

He sang Cock Robin's love
    To the little Jenny Wren,
And when he got unto the end,
    Then he began again.

PUNCH AND JUDY

Punch and Judy
  Fought for a pie,
Punch gave Judy
  A knock in the eye.

Says Punch to Judy,
  "Will you have any more?"
Says Judy to Punch,
  "My eye is too sore."

THREE CHILDREN SLIDING

Three children slid-
ing on the ice
　　Upon a summer's
day,
As it fell out, they all
fell in,
　　The rest they ran
away.

O! had these children
been at school,
　　Or sliding on dry
ground,
Ten thousand pounds to
one penny
　　They had not then
been drown'd.

Ye parents who have children dear,
And eke ye that have none,
If you would have them safe abroad,
Pray keep them safe at home.

THE LITTLE BIRD

Once I saw a little bird
   Come hop, hop, hop;
So I cried, "Little bird,
   Will you stop, stop, stop?"

And was going to the window
   To say, "How do you do?"
But he shook his little tail,
   And far away he flew.

TOAD AND FROG

"Croak," said the toad, "I'm hungry I think,
To-day I've had nothing to eat or to drink;
I'll crawl to a garden and jump through the pales,
And there I'll dine nicely on slugs and on snails."

"Ho, ho!" quoth the frog, "is that what you mean?
Then I'll hop away to the next meadow stream,
There I will drink, and eat worms and slugs too,
And then I shall have a good dinner like you."

BRIAN O'LIN

Brian O'Lin had no breeches to wear,
So he bought him a sheep-skin and made him a pair,
With the skinny side out, and the woolly side in,
"Ah, ha, that is warm!" said Brian O'Lin.

Brian O'Lin and his wife and wife's mother,
They all went over a bridge together;
The bridge was broken and they all fell in,
"Mischief take all!" quoth Brian O'Lin.

JACK SPRAT

Jack Sprat
Could eat no fat,
His wife could eat no lean;
And so betwixt them both
They licked the platter clean.

OF WASHING

They that was on Friday, was in need;
And they that was on Saturday, oh! they're sluts indeed.

Jack Sprat and his wife

OLD MOTHER GOOSE

Old Mother Goose, when
  She wanted to wander,
Would ride through the air
  On a very fine gander.

Mother Goose had a house,
  'T was built in a wood,
Where an owl at the door
  For sentinel stood.

She had a son Jack,
  A plain-looking lad,
he was not very good,
  Nor yet very bad.

She sent him to market,
  A live goose he bought;
"Here, Mother," says he,
  "It will not go for nought."

Jack's goose and her gander
  Grew very fond;
They'd both eat together,
  Or swim in one pond.

Jack found one morning,
  As I have been told,
His goose had laid him
  An egg of pure gold.

Jack ran to his mother,
  The news for to tell,
She called him a good boy,
  And said it was well.

Then Jack went a-courting
  A lady so gay,
As fair as the lily,
  As sweet as the May.

A Rogue and the Squire
  Came behind his back,
And began to belabour
  The sides of poor Jack.

Then old Mother Goose
  That instant came in,
And turned her son Jack
  Into famed Harlequin.

She then with her wand
  Touched the lady so fine,
And turned her at once
  Into sweet Columbine.

The gold egg into
  The sea was thrown then,—
When Jack jumped in,
  And got the egg back again.

The Rogue got the goose,
  Which he vowed he would kill,
Resolving at once
  His pockets to fill.

Jack's mother came in,
  And caught the goose soon,
And mounting its back,
  Flew up to the moon.

THE OBSTINATE PIG

An old woman was sweeping her house, and she found a little crooked sixpence.

"What," said she, "shall I do with this little sixpence? I will go to market, and buy a little pig."

As she was coming home she came to a stile; but Piggy would not go over the stile.

She went a little farther and she met a
    dog. So she said to the dog:
  "Dog, dog, bite pig! Piggy won't get
    over the stile;
And I sha'n't get home to-night."

  But the dog would not.

She went a little farther and she met a stick.
  So she said:

"Stick, stick, beat dog!
Dog won't bite pig;
Pig won't get over the stile;
And I sha'n't get home to-night."

But the stick would not.

She went a little farther and she met a fire.
  So she said:
    "Fire, fire, burn stick!
    Stick won't beat dog;
    Dog won't bite pig;
    Pig won't get over the stile;
    And I sha'n't get home to-night."

But the fire would not.

She went a little farther and she met some water.
So she said:
"Water, water, quench fire!
Fire won't burn stick;
Stick won't beat dog;
Dog won't bite pig;
Pig won't get over the stile;
And I sha'n't get home to-night."

But the water would not.

She went a little farther and she met an ox.
So she said:
"Ox, ox, drink water!
Water won't quench fire;
Fire won't burn stick;
Stick won't beat dog;
Dog won't bite pig;
Pig won't get over the stile;
And I sha'n't get home to-night."

But the ox would not.

She went a little farther and she met a butcher.
  So she said:
    "Butcher, butcher, kill ox!
    Ox won't drink water;
    Water won't quench fire;
    Fire won't burn stick;
    Stick won't beat dog;
    Dog won't bite pig;
    Pig won't get over the stile;
    And I sha'n't get home to-night."

But the butcher would not.

She went a little farther and she met a rope.
  So she said:
    "Rope, rope, hang butcher!
    Butcher won't kill ox;
    Ox won't drink water;
    Water won't quench fire;
    Fire won't burn stick;
    Stick won't beat dog;
    Dog won't bite pig;
    Pig won't get over the stile;
    And I sha'n't get home to-night."

But the rope would not.

She went a little farther and she met a rat.
   So she said:
      "Rat, rat, gnaw rope!
      Rope won't hang butcher;
      Butcher won't kill ox;
      Ox won't drink water;
      Water won't quench fire;
      Fire won't burn stick;
      Stick won't beat dog;
      Dog won't bite pig;
      Pig won't get over the stile;
      And I sha'n't get home to-night."

But the rat would not.

She went a little farther and she met a cat.
   So she said:
      "Cat, cat, kill rat!
      Rat won't gnaw rope;
      Rope won't hang butcher;
      Butcher won't kill ox;
      Ox won't drink water;
      Water won't quench fire;
      Fire won't burn stick;

Stick won't beat dog;
Dog won't bite pig;
Pig won't get over the stile;
And I sha'n't get home to-night."

The cat said: "If you will get me a saucer of milk from the cow in yonder field I will kill the rat."

So the old woman went to the cow and said: "Cow, cow, will you give me a saucer of milk?"

And the cow said: "If you will get me a bucket full of water from yonder brook I will give you the milk." And the old woman took the bucket to the brook; but the water all rushed out through the holes in the bottom.

So she filled the holes up with stones, got the water, and took it to the cow, who at once gave her the saucer of milk. Then the old woman gave the cat the milk, and when she had lapped up the milk—

The cat began to kill the rat;
The rat began to gnaw the rope;
The rope began to hang the butcher;
The butcher began to kill the ox;
The ox began to drink the water;
The water began to quench the fire;
The fire began to burn the stick;
The stick began to beat the dog;
The dog began to bite the pig;
The pig jumped over the stile;
And so the old woman go home that night.

SHAVE A PIG

Barber, barber, shave a pig,
How many hairs will make a wig?
"Four and twenty, that's enough,"
Give the barber a pinch of snuff.

FORTUNE-TELLING BY CHERRIES STONES

One, I love; two, I love;
Three, I love, I say;
Four, I love with all my
    heart;
Five, I cast away;
Six, he loves; seven she
    loves;
Eight, both love;
Nine, he comes; ten, he
    tarries;
Eleven, he courts; and
    twelve, he marries.

THE HARE AND THE TORTOISE

This is a tale that, though extremely old,
Still pleases simple people when it 's told.
And having written it in rhyme anew
I shall repeat the story here for you.
The hare, who 'd often proved his wondrous pace,
Challenged the tortoise, chaffing, to a race.
The tortoise in a sporting way agreed
For he had spirit, though not built for speed.
The other creatures came to watch the race,
Smiles of amusement wreathing every face;
The tortoise they all thought absurd to dare
To try to race a creature like the hare.
Well, off they set. The hare disdained to run,
But, having called his friends to see the fun,
Laughed at the tortoise plodding down the track,
Bearing his shelly house upon his back.
The hare grew bored; the sun was very strong;
"This race," he thought, "is lasting far too long.
While tortoise trudges on I'll have a nap,
And then I'll overtake the poor old chap."
He stopped, he dozed; ere long he soundly slept,
While steadily the stout old tortoise stepped.
So, when the hare awoke, the race was done,

And, wonderful to tell, he had not won!
Their jokes the other creatures did not spare,
Oh, how they chaffed the now crestfallen hare!
(It is the same amongst us human folks—
Those who look on are far too free with jokes.)

MORAL

Learn from this tale, it does not do to take
Your forty winks while rivals are awake.

THE HERON AND THE FISH

One day—it doesn't matter when or where—a heron, which had been flying along a valley, looked down and saw a beautiful river flowing beneath him. Swiftly he descended from the air, and alighting on the bank, waded on his long legs into the water to fish. As he stood there without a movement he looked just like a tall post, and soon the fish ceased to take any notice of him, and swam to and fro close by without any fear.

Now this heron was not very hungry, and he was rather a faddy bird. So that though many common fish, like pike and tench and gudgeon, were within reach of his long beak, with which he could have caught one at any moment, he kept waiting.

" All these are very well," he said to himself, " but I want something much daintier and finer. Perhaps a young salmon or a pretty spotted trout will come presently—then I will catch him for my dinner."

Presently an eel swam wriggling past his feet. The heron looked at it, but did not catch it. No, something nicer was sure to come. By and by several frogs swam near, but still he delayed. " What are mere frogs?" he said to himself. " Very plain feeding for such a bird as myself."

While he stood thinking thus, hours passed by, and all the

The Dainty Heron

fish he had despised swam away. Then he suddenly began to feel very hungry, and would have given anything even for an eel. But look as keenly as he might, not one was to be seen, and by and by he had to be content to eat a wretched little snail, which was crawling over a stone on the bank, for his supper.

MORAL

If food you fuss too much about
Some day you'll have to go without.

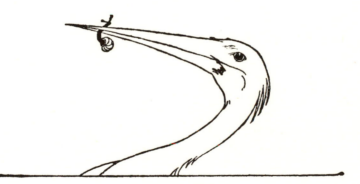

THE THREE BEARS

Once upon a time three bears lived in a cottage near a wood.

And in a house on the other side of the wood a little girl lived with her parents.

One of the bears was a **GREAT BIG BEAR**.

One was a MIDDLE-SIZED BEAR.

And one was a TINY WEE BEAR.

The little girl had Iong golden hair, so she was called Goldilocks.

One day the three bears went for a walk in the wood, while their breakfast porridge was cooling; and while they were gone Goldilocks, who was also in the wood, came to their cottage. Noticing that the door was open, she peeped in; and there she saw a table upon which were three bowls of porridge.

One of the bowls was a **GREAT BIG BOWL**.

One was a MIDDLE-SIZED BOWL.

And one was a TINY WEE BOWL.

Set round the table were three chairs.

One of the chairs was a **GREAT BIG CHAIR**.

One was a MIDDLE-SIZED CHAIR.

And one was a TINY WEE CHAIR.

Goldilocks looked about, but she saw no one, and so she went into the cottage.

And being hungry, she took up a great big spoon, and helped herself to some porridge from the great big bowl. But she quickly dropped the spoon, for the porridge was too hot, and had burned her tongue.

Then she took up a middle-sized spoon, and helped herself to some porridge from the middle-sized bowl.

But she quickly dropped that spoon also, for the porridge was too cold.

And last she took up a tiny wee spoon, and helped herself to some porridge from the tiny wee bowl. Now, the porridge in that bowl was just right, neither too hot nor too cold. So Goldilocks ate it all up.

Then, being tired, she sat down in the great big chair. But she quickly jumped up again, for the great big cushion in it was too hard.

After that she sat down in the middle-sized chair. But again she quickly jumped up, for the middle-sized cushion in it was too soft.

And last, she sat down in the tiny wee chair. And the tiny wee cushion in the tiny wee chair was just right. So Goldilocks went on sitting upon it till the bottom of the chair fell out, and the cushion with it, and she found herself sitting upon the floor.

Then she looked this way and that way, and in one corner of the cottage she noticed some steep stairs.

So she went up the steep stairs, and then into a little bedroom.

And there she saw three beds. One of the beds was a GREAT BIG BED. One was a MIDDLE-SIZED BED. And one was a TINY WEE BED.

Being sleepy, Goldilocks lay down upon the great big bed.

But she quickly got up again, for the head of the great big bed was too high.

Then she lay down upon the middle-sized bed; but again she quickly got up, for the foot of the middle-sized bed was too low.

And last, she lay down upon the tiny wee bed. Now, the tiny wee bed was just right, so very soon Goldilocks was fast asleep upon it.

When she had fallen asleep, the three bears came home from their walk in the wood.

First, the Great Big Bear spied his great big spoon standing in his great big bowl.

"SOMEONE HAS BEEN TASTING MY POR-RIDGE," roared he.

Then the Middle-sized Bear spied her middle-sized spoon standing in her middle-sized bowl.

"SOMEONE HAS BEEN TASTING MY PORRIDGE," growled she.

And last, the Tiny Wee Bear spied his tiny wee spoon standing in his empty, tiny wee bowl.

"SOMEONE HAS BEEN TASTING MY PORRIDGE," squeaked he, "AND HAS EATEN IT ALL UP."

By this time the Great Big Bear had noticed that the great big cushion that lay in his great big chair was rumpled.

"SOMEONE HAS BEEN SITTING IN MY CHAIR," roared he.

Then the Middle-sized Bear noticed that the middle-sized cushion that lay in her middlesized chair was rumpled.

"SOMEONE HAS BEEN SITTING IN MY CHAIR," growled she.

And last, the Tiny Wee Bear noticed that the tiny wee cushion of his tiny wee chair lay upon the floor.

"SOMEONE HAS BEEN SITTING IN MY CHAIR," squeaked he, "AND HAS SAT THE BOTTOM OUT."

The three bears looked this way and that way, but saw no one, and so they went up the steep stairs into the bedroom.

And there the Great Big Bear immediately noticed that the bedclothes which covered his great big bed were crumpled.

"SOMEONE HAS BEEN LYING ON MY BED," roared he.

Then the Middle-sized Bear saw that the bedclothes on her middle-sized bed were crumpled.

"SOMEONE HAS BEEN LYING ON MY BED," growled she.

And last, the Tiny Wee Bear saw that the bedclothes on his tiny wee bed were in a heap.

"SOMEONE HAS BEEN LYING ON MY BED," squeaked he, "AND HERE SHE IS!"

Goldilocks was very much frightened. She jumped from the tiny wee bed and darted down the stairs, with her golden hair flying around her head.

And the three bears were so dazzled by the brightness of her hair that they stumbled as they ran after her down the stairs.

When they reached the kitchen, Goldilocks had run out of the cottage door; and when they reached the door, she was a long way off. And though they ran and ran they did not catch her, for she had run right through the wood, and was safe at home with her parents.

So the three bears went back to their cottage.

THE LION AND THE MOUSE

One day a lion, having nothing better to do, caught a mouse, and was about to pop the tiny creature into his mouth, when in its squeaky voice it pled with the lion for its life.

"Let me go, O mighty King of Beasts!" it cried. "I am no meal for you."

"How dare you speak to me?" growled the lion.

"Because you are the King of Beasts," answered the mouse, "and so are bound to listen."

"Suppose I choose to eat you just for fun?" said the lion.

"That is surely beneath your dignity," answered the mouse. "If you do eat me you will be just as hungry afterwards. Apart from that, if you let me go alive, the day may come when I shall be able to do you a good turn."

This idea so much amused the mighty creature that, laughing loudly, he let the mouse run off.

Some time after this, in the same part of the forest, the lion ran into a net spread in his path by hunters. At once he became entangled, and the more he struggled, the more firmly he was held.

At last in despair he ceased his efforts, and lay still, thinking his end was come and that as his own strength could not free him, he was doomed. Then in the silence he heard the voice of the mouse. "Here I am," it said; "if you will keep quiet I will soon set you free, for I have not lost my gratitude."

And with that it set about nibbling through the cords of the net, and soon its sharp little teeth had cut so many that with one great heave the lion broke the rest and was free once more.

MORAL

Never despise a humble friend;
Perhaps he'll save you in the end.

RED RIDING-HOOD

Once upon a time, in a cottage near a wood, there lived a little girl.

Her grandmother, who lived in a cottage on the other side of the wood, made a beautiful red hood for her, which suited her so well that everybody called her Red Riding-Hood.

One day Red Riding-Hood's mother said to her: "My dear, I have heard that your grandmother has been ill, so I want you to take her this basket, which has in it some cream and eggs, and a little pat of butter.

"Go straight there and back, and do not play or idle, and do not talk to anyone by the way."

So Red Riding-Hood put on her hood, took the basket on her arm, and started off at once. But instead of going by the road, as her mother had told her to do, she went through the wood.

And in the wood she met an old wolf.

Now this wolf was afraid to eat her, because some wood-cutters were not far off.

So he stopped her, and said:

"What have you in your basket, my dear?"

Then Red Riding-Hood, who forgot that her mother had told her she must not talk to anyone by the way, replied:

"Some cream. and some eggs, and a little pat of butter, for my Granny."

"Where does Granny live, my dear?"

"In the cottage beyond the wood."

"And what do you do when you get to the cottage, my dear?"

"I knock at the door."

"And what does your Granny do then, my dear?"

"She says: 'Who is there?'"

"And what do you do next, my dear?"

"I say: 'I am Red Riding-Hood, Granny.'"

"And what does Granny do next, my dear?"

"She cries out: 'Pull the bobbin, and the latch will go up'."

When the wolf heard this. he ran off as fast as he could to the grandmother's cottage.

The wolf was not long in reaching the grandmother's cottage, and went at once to the door and knocked at it gently.

"Who is there?" said a voice from within.

"I am Red Riding-Hood," said the wolf, in a squeaky voice which he tried to make as like the little girl's as he could.

Hearing that, the grandmother, who was ill and in bed, called out:

"Pull the bobbin, and the latch will go up."

The wolf pulled the bobbin, the latch went up, and the door opened.

Then the wolf ran into the cottage, and gobbled up the old woman.

Then he shut the door again, and putting on the grandmother's nightgown and nightcap and spectacles, he got into bed to wait for Red Riding-Hood.

He had not long to wait.

In a little while the child came to the door and knocked tap, tap.

"Who is there?" asked the wolf, making his voice as soft as he could.

"I am Red Riding-Hood, and I have brought you some cream and eggs, and a little pat of butter," said the child.

"Pull the bobbin, and the latch will go up," cried the wolf.

Then Red Riding-Hood pulled the bobbin, and the latch went up; the door opened, and she stepped into the cottage.

The wolf drew the bedclothes up round his head, so that the little girl could not see him very well, and said: "Shut the door, and sit down beside me, my dear."

So Red Riding-Hood shut the door, and sat down close to the bed.

And when she saw how strange her grandmother looked, she was astonished, and said:

"Oh, Grandmamma, what great arms you have got!"

"All the better to hug you, my dear," replied the wolf.

Red Riding-Hood was quiet for a little while, and then said:

"Oh, Grandmamma, what great ears you have got!"

"All the better to hear you, my dear."

"Oh, Grandmamma, what great eyes you have got!" said Red Riding-Hood, after another short pause.

"All the better to see you, my dear."

Red Riding-Hood looked again in a little while, and then said:

"Oh, Grandmamma, what great teeth you have got!"

"All the better to eat you, my dear."

And as he said that, the wicked wolf sprang up in bed to seize the little girl and gobble her up.

But at that moment the door of the cottage opened, and a woodcutter ran in.

He was Red Riding-Hood's father, who had seen his daughter go to her grandmother's cottage, and had come to take her home.

He soon chopped off the wicked wolf's head with his axe, and then he lifted poor Red Riding-Hood in his arms.

The little girl was very much frightened, and threw her arms round her father's neck and cried bitterly.

Then the woodcutter, holding her very tightly to make her feel quite safe, carried her home.

And as he went along, he sang to her these wise words:

> "A little maid
> Must be afraid
> To do other than her mother told her;
> Of idling must be wary,
> Of gossiping be chary,
> She'll learn prudence by the time that she is older."

CINDERELLA

Once upon a time there was a man, a widower, who, marrying again, took for his second wife a very proud woman.

This woman, who was a widow, had two daughters, as proud as herself. Her second husband had one daughter, who was gentle and good, as her mother had been.

The new wife hated her young stepdaughter, because her gentle ways and the sweetness of her temper, which was shown in her beautiful face, made the ill manners and frowning faces of her own daughters appear as disagreeable and ugly as they really were.

So she set her to do all the meanest work of the house.

The young girl swept, and baked, and washed for the

whole household. She wore only shabby clothes, and slept in a bare garret.

However, she did not complain, but bore all with patience.

And when her work was finished, she would sit down among the cinders in the chimney-corner. So her stepsisters, who were also unkind to her, gave her the name of Cinderella.

Now, it happened that the King's son made up his mind to give a ball, and to invite to it all the people of fashion in that countryside. There was to be dancing for two evenings, and the supper and entertainment were to be of a very splendid kind.

Cinderella's stepsisters were invited; and very proud and happy they were, as they talked of the smart dresses they would wear, and the grand folk they would meet at the palace.

"I shall look well in blue satin, with a feather in my hair," said the elder sister.

"None will be finer than I, in my red-and-gold velvet, with my plumed turban," said the younger.

Cinderella listened sadly to their talk, for she too would have liked to go to the palace to wear a beautiful dress, and to join in the merry-making.

When the great day came, Cinderella was busy from morning till evening helping her stepsisters to get ready for the ball.

She laced their gowns, dressed their hair, arranged their feathers and jewels, and even put on their slippers for them.

And while she did so, they teased her, to amuse themselves.

"Would you not like to go to the ball, Cinderella?" they asked.

"I think that in my shabby frock I should be out of place in the King's palace," replied Cinderella gently.

"Yes, indeed," said her stepsisters, laughing. "A cinderwench at a ball would make all the world stare and mock."

At last the sisters were ready, and with their mother they drove away to the palace.

When they were gone, Cinderella, left alone, sat down among the cinders and began to cry.

"Oh! I wish—I wish—" she sobbed.

"What do you wish?" asked a kind voice.

Cinderella was so much startled that she left off crying.

She looked up and saw, standing before her, an old lady, wearing a red cloak and a pointed hat, and leaning on a stick.

Cinderella knew this old lady to be her Godmother, who was a fairy.

"I can guess what you wish," said the fairy Godmother. "You wish to go to the ball at the palace."

"Yes, indeed I do, dear Godmother," cried Cinderella eagerly.

"Well, so you shall," replied the old lady. "You are a good girl, and you deserve to be happy. So dry your eyes and do as I tell you, and you shall be at the ball in next to no time."

Cinderella, all smiles now, jumped up from her stool by the hearth.

"Run into the garden," her Godmother went on, "and fetch me the largest pumpkin you can find."

Away went Cinderella, and very soon she ran back, hugging a big yellow pumpkin. The fairy Godmother scooped out the inside of the pumpkin, leaving nothing but the rind. This she touched with her stick, which was really a fairy wand, and at once the pumpkin rind became a fine white coach, decorated with gold and lined with yellow.

"Now fetch the mouse-trap," said she, and Cinderella obeyed quickly.

In the mouse-trap were six mice. The fairy Godmother opened the trap, and as each mouse ran out she touched it with her wand, and it became a sleek and prancing horse.

"Now get the rat-trap," said she.

So Cinderella brought the rat-trap, in which there were three rats.

The fairy Godmother chose the finest of the three rats, and touched it with her wand. And immediately the animal turned

into a tall and handsomely-dressed coachman.

"Behind the watering-pot are six green lizards," said the fairy Godmother; "bring them here."

Cinderella brought the six lizards, and at a touch of the fairy Godmother's wand each one was changed into a smart footman, in a splendid uniform. The coachman mounted the box, and a footman climbed to the back of the coach, while another held the door open for Cinderella.

"Now your carriage is ready," said the fairy Godmother.

"But how can I go to the ball like this?" asked Cinderella, looking down at the shabby frock she was wearing.

"You shall soon be more beautiful than your coach," replied her Godmother, and she tapped her lightly on the head with her wand.

Then Cinderella's old clothes were turned into robes of silk and velvet, glittering with jewels.

And the fairy Godmother gave her a beautiful little pair of shining glass slippers, the prettiest that ever were seen.

So, with splendid clothes and a happy heart, Cinderella stepped into her coach.

"Remember," said her Godmother, "you must leave the ball before the clock strikes twelve. If you do not, your coach will again become a pumpkin rind, your horses will become mice, your coachman will turn into a rat, and your footmen into lizards; while you will find yourself once more in your shabby old clothes."

Cinderella promised to remember. Then the coachman whipped up his horses, the footmen held up their heads and clung to the back of the coach, and away they went.

When the coach drove up to the palace, the Prince, who had been told that a great princess had arrived, came out to receive Cinderella, and to lead her into the ball-room.

As she entered, the musicians ceased playing, and the dancers stopped dancing, while all gazed in surprise at the lovely, unknown princess.

All the evening, the Prince kept at Cinderella's side, dancing and talking with her.

When a clock chimed the quarter before twelve, Cinderella rose, and after curtsying to the company, left the palace immediately, and drove home in her coach.

When her stepsisters returned they told the young girl of the beautiful princess who had been at the ball, for they had not recognized her there.

"She paid us a great deal of attention," said they; "and no one knows who she is, though the Prince admires her so much that he would give half his kingdom to find out."

Cinderella smiled.

"How much I should like to see this princess!" said she. "Will you, dear sisters, lend me a dress, so that I too may go to the ball to-morrow?"

"You go, indeed!" sneered her stepsisters. "A fine figure you would be at a ball! We would not be seen with you."

On the next evening, the stepsisters again went to the palace.

And Cinderella went too, in her coach, even more beautifully dressed than before. The Prince again kept close beside

her, and said so many kind things to her that Cinderella, in her happiness, forgot how quickly the hours flew past.

She thought it not yet eleven, when the clock struck twelve.

Then she started in affright, and fled from the ballroom as swiftly as a deer.

The Prince ran after her, but did not catch her; and all he could find of her was a little glass slipper, lying on the staircase.

The guards said that no one had passed through the palace gates but a little kitchen-wench in shabby clothes. Nor had they seen the princess's coach drive away, although it was gone from the palace courtyard. Where it had stood lay a hol-

low pumpkin rind, which no one had noticed before; and in the palace larder a fine rat and six mice were enjoying themselves, while six little green lizards crept into sheltered crannies in the stone wall of the palace garden.

While the Prince was searching the palace for Cinderella, she was running home, breathless, in her old clothes, with none of her finery left but one little glass slipper.

When her stepsisters returned home, they were in quite a flutter of excitement about what had happened at the ball.

They told Cinderella that the beautiful princess had been there again, and that just as the clock struck twelve she had run from the hall and disappeared, dropping one of her glass slippers in her haste.

"The Prince himself picked it up," said they; "and so much is he in love with the wearer of it that he has vowed to marry her whom it will exactly fit."

Next morning folk were roused by the sound of trumpets, as through the streets of the town came the royal chamberlain, with guards, and an attendant carrying the little glass slipper on a velvet cushion.

From house to house they went; and everywhere the slipper was tried upon the feet of all the young women in the house, were they princesses, court ladies, citizens' daughters, or only poor cottage-wenches.

But no foot was found which the slipper fitted.

So by and by the royal chamberlain arrived at the house of Cinderella's father.

Cinderella's stepsisters were in great haste to try on the slipper. But though they pinched their toes and squeezed their heels, their feet were far too large to go into it.

Then the royal chamberlain inquired whether there were any other young women in the house.

"Only a cinder-wench," said the elder of Cinderella's stepsisters. "It would only be wasting time to trouble with her."

"Let her be brought here," ordered the royal chamberlain.

So Cinderella was sent for, and, sitting down in a chair, stretched out her foot.

"Impertinence" "Ridiculous nonsense!" cried both her stepsisters at once.

But the royal chamberlain stooped down, and put the slipper to Cinderella's foot. And of course, as it was her very own, it slipped on as easily as possible, and fitted exactly.

Then, to the surprise of everyone, Cinderella drew the other little glass slipper from her pocket, and put that on also.

And at that moment the fairy Godmother appeared, and, with a touch of her wand, changed Cinderella's poor garments into beautiful robes, more splendid than ever.

And then everyone saw that she was indeed the beautiful princess whom the Prince loved.

The stepsisters fell at her feet, and begged her forgiveness.

And Cinderella freely forgave them, and asked them to try to love her.

The news quickly spread through the town, and soon the Prince arrived at the house, and greeted Cinderella joyfully.

Then she was taken to the palace, and they were married that day.

Soon afterwards, Cinderella fetched her stepsisters to live at the palace.

They were so much ashamed of their past conduct, and so grateful for her kindness, that they ceased to be proud and unkind.

And, as their hearts became good, their faces became beautiful.

Then two lords of the Court married them, and they, like Cinderella, were happy.

THE THREE LITTLE PIGS

ONCE upon a time there were three little pigs whose mother was too poor to give them all as much food as they wanted. So, when they were big enough to take care of themselves, she turned them out of the home-sty to find their own living.

As the first little pig trudged through the world, seeking his fortune, he met a man carrying a truss of straw. And because of his good manners the man gave him the truss of straw, and the little pig built a house with it, and sat down inside.

By and by a wolf came along, and, smelling the pig, said: "Little Pig, Little Pig, let me come in."

But the pig knew the wolf's voice, so he replied: "No, no, by the hair on my chinny-chin-chin!"

"Then," said the wolf, "I'll huff, and I'll puff and I'll blow your house in." So he huffed, and he puffed, till he blew the house of straw in; and then he ate up the little pig.

As the second little pig trudged through the world, seeking his fortune, he met a man carrying a bundle of furze.

"If you please, sir," said he, "will you give me that furze to build a house with?"

And because he was polite the man gave him the bundle of

furze, and the little pig built a house, and sat down inside it.

By and by the wolf came along, and saw the house, and smelt the pig. Then he knocked at the door, and said: "Little Pig, Little Pig, let me come in."

But the pig peeped through the keyhole and saw the wolf's ears, so he replied: "No, no, by the hair on my chinny-chin-chin!"

"Then," said the wolf, "I'll huff, and I'll puff, and I'll blow your house in." So he huffed and he puffed, and he huffed and he puffed, till at last he blew the house of furze in; and then he ate up the little pig.

As the third little pig trudged through the world, seeking his fortune, he met a man carrying a load of bricks.

"If you please, sir," said he, "will you give me those bricks to build a house with?"

And because he was well-behaved the man gave him the load of bricks, and the little pig built a house, and sat down inside it.

By and by the

wolf came along, and saw the house, and smelt the pig. Then he knocked at the door, and said:

"Little Pig, Little Pig, let me come in."

But the pig peeped through the crack under the door, and saw the wolf's paws, so he replied, as his brothers had done: "No, no, by the hair on my chinny-chin-chin!"

"Then," said the wolf, "I'll huff, and I'll puff, and I'll blow your house in." So he huffed and he puffed and he huffed and he puffed, and he huffed and he puffed till he was out of breath; but he could not blow the house of bricks in. And when he saw that after all his huffing and puffing the house stood firm, he said: "Little Pig, Little Pig, I can tell you where there are some nice turnips."

"Where?" asked the little pig, still safe inside.

"In the field at the top of the lane," replied the cunning wolf; "and if you will be ready at six o'clock to-morrow morning, we will get some for dinner."

"Yes, I will be ready," said the little pig.

Next day, the little pig got up at five o'clock, and ran

quickly to the field at the top of the lane and found some nice turnips, which he took home for dinner.

At six o'clock the wolf knocked at the door, and said: "Little Pig, I am waiting for you."

"Pray don't wait any longer," replied the little pig, "for I have been to the field and come back, and I have a big dish of nice turnips for dinner."

When the wolf heard this he felt very angry, but he made his voice smooth, and said: "Little Pig, Little Pig, I know where there are some nice apples."

"Where?" asked the little pig, without opening the door.

"On a tree at the bottom of the lane," replied the wolf; "and if you will be ready at five o'clock to-morrow morning, I will take you there, and we will get some for dinner."

"Yes, I will be ready," said the little pig.

Next day, the little pig got up at four o'clock, and hurried to the bottom of the lane and climbed the apple tree. He had picked a lot of nice apples, and was just going to jump down

and run home, when he saw the wolf coming. So he stayed where he was, feeling very frightened. The wolf came to the foot of the tree, and grinned till he showed all his sharp teeth.

"Little Pig," said he, "why did you not wait for me?"

"I was so hungry that I could not wait," replied the little pig. "Let me throw you down one of the apples, that you may taste it, and see how nice they are." And he threw an apple so far that while the wolf was gone to pick it up he had time to jump down from the tree and run away home.

Next day the wolf came again to the pig's house, and knocked at the door, and said: "Little Pig, Little Pig, there is to be a fair on the hill this afternoon. Will you go with me?"

"Yes," replied the little pig, "I will go. What time will you call for me?"

"At three o'clock," replied the wolf.

But, as usual, the little pig started before the wolf came, and visited the fair, where he bought a butter-churn. He was carrying it home, when he saw the wolf a long way off, trotting up the hill. Then, as he was very frightened, and could think of nothing better to do, he hid himself in the churn. But as he jumped in, the churn fell on its side, and began to roll over and over down the hill, with the pig inside.

The wolf, seeing a strange round thing coming towards him, was so much alarmed that he ran away home as fast as his legs would take him, without visiting the fair.

At the bottom of the hill the little pig got out of the churn, and went into his house; and soon after he was safely inside, the wolf knocked at the door, and said: "Little Pig, I could not go to the fair, for a great round thing ran after me down the hill, and drove me home."

"Ha!" replied the little pig with a chuckle, "that was my butter-churn, which I bought at the fair; and I was inside it."

Then the wolf was very angry, and declared that he would climb down the chimney of the house, and eat the little pig up; and he began to scramble on to the roof. But while he did this, the little pig stirred the fire to a blaze, and hung a large pot full of water over it. And when he heard a noise in the chimney, he lifted the lid of the pot, and the wolf tumbled into the water with a splash. Then the little pig boiled him, and ate him for supper. And after that he lived happily for the rest of his life in the house of bricks.